The Roots of Language Series

Wordstrength
Using Roots and Prefixes

by Joan Robinson

Fearon Teacher Aids
A Division of Frank Schaffer Publications, Inc.

Illustrator: Marilynn Barr

Gratitude is extended to Barbara Morris, art teacher in Ridgewood, New Jersey, for her creative ideas upon which many of the illustrations for these pages are based.

© **Fearon Teacher Aids**
A Division of Frank Schaffer Publications, Inc.
23740 Hawthorne Boulevard
Torrance, CA 90505-5927

ISBN 0-8224-7451-4

Contents

Introduction

More than 450 million people around the world speak English. (The only language used by more people is Mandarin Chinese.) English is an amalgam of many other languages, including French, Spanish, German, Dutch, Italian, Swedish, Norwegian, and Arabic. Nearly 60 percent of English words, however, are derived from Latin directly, or indirectly through Old French. Greek has also had a strong influence on English because many Latin words are derived from Greek, an earlier language than Latin. Much of our scientific and mathematical language has been coined from Greek elements.

Acquainting your students with Latin and Greek prefixes and roots will help them decode new words wherever they encounter them—in stories or in social studies or science texts (an octopus has eight legs, so an octagon must have eight sides). This knowledge will also help them use words precisely. They'll know the difference between precede and proceed, emigrant and immigrant, and deductive and inductive.

How to Use This Book

This vocabulary program, which can be used with students from grade 4 to grade 9, is the result of 18 years of teaching experience. Each of the 30 lessons is self-contained on two reproducible pages. The first page introduces a common Latin or Greek prefix or root with

- a list of five to six words—some familiar, some new, but none obscure—that use the prefix or root,
- the most common definition of each word, and
- illustrations that bring the words to life.

The second page contains exercises to help students master the prefix or root and

the words introduced on the first page. Sections A and B help the students to become familiar with the root or prefix and to review the definitions of the words. Section C activities require creativity and critical thinking.

A pretest shows students what they have to learn. Three review tests along the way give them practice using their new prefix- and root-based vocabulary. There is also a final test using words and prefixes from the entire book. The answer key at the end of the book includes the answers for all the exercise pages and all the tests. To help your class understand how Latin and Greek elements were incorporated into English, see the following section, "A Brief History of the Greek and Latin Roots of English."

This book begins with several lessons about numerical prefixes. You can easily show your students how the prefix affects the meaning of a root word. (Do you want a centigram or a decagram of ice cream?) Used at the rate of one lesson or test a week, this book can take you through the entire year. However you choose to use *Wordstrength*, your students are sure to benefit from gaining familiarity with the roots of language.

A Brief History of the Greek and Latin Roots of English

Scholars explain the prevalence of Latin and Greek elements in the English language by looking at English history. In A.D. 43 the Romans (who took much of their language from the Greeks) conquered the Celts of Britain and held power until the middle of the 400s. In spite of their resistance, the Celts adopted some Latin words during those centuries.

When the Germanic tribes—the Jutes, the Angles, and the Saxons—invaded Britain in the fifth century, they brought more Latin-based words. These words had been incorporated into the Germanic languages when the Romans visited the lands of the tribes on the European continent. Many of these were practical words—such as *cheese, butter, pound,* and *inch*—for products and concepts that the Romans introduced to the Germanic tribes.

With the spread of Christianity in the British Isles in the 600s came a whole host of Latinate words—such as *monk, creed, verse, temple,* and *candle*—because Latin was the language of the Church.

When the Normans, led by William the Conqueror, invaded England in 1066, they brought their French language, which came from Latin, and added some 10,000 words to English—words of nobility and feudalism, such as *palace, throne, enemy, army, soldier, castle, fashion,* and *beauty.*

In the fifteenth century, the Renaissance revived the Greek and Roman classics, which became more widely available because of the invention of the printing press. Latin became almost a second language for scholars and scientists. To be taken seriously, they had to write their books in Latin. (Today, lawyers and doctors still use Latin.) Not surprisingly, Latin words poured into the English language during the Renaissance.

To explore the history of the English language further, consult an encyclopedia or any of the following books:

Burriss, Eli E., and Lionel Casson. *Latin and Greek in Current Use.* 2d ed. Englewood Cliffs, NJ: Prentice Hall, 1949.

Ernst, Margaret S. *Words: English Roots and How They Grow.* 3d ed. rev. New York: Knopf, 1957.

Funk, Wilfred. *Word Origins and Their Romantic Stories.* 1950. New York: Bell, 1978.

Morris, William, and Mary Morris. *Morris Dictionary of Word and Phrase Origins.* New York: Harper and Row, 1977.

Paisner, Milton. *One Word Leads to Another: A Light History of Words.* New York: Dembner Books, 1982.

Sarnoff, Jane. *Words: A Book About the Origins of Everyday Words.* New York: Scribner, 1981.

The following dictionaries provide useful etymologies for individual words:

American Heritage Dictionary of the English Language. Ed. William Morris. Boston: Houghton Mifflin, 1969.

Webster's New World Dictionary. 2d college ed. Ed. David B. Guralnik. New York: Prentice Hall, 1986.

Webster's Ninth New Collegiate Dictionary. Ed. Frederick C. Mish. Springfield, MA: Merriam-Webster, 1985.

Name _____

Pretest

A. Match the following numerical prefixes with their meaning. (Some prefixes have the same meaning.) Write the number of the answer in the blank beside the prefix.

___ bi-	___ milli-	1. one
___ cent-	___ mono-	2. two
___ centi-	___ penta-	3. three
___ deca-	___ quadr-	4. four
___ deci-	___ quint-	5. five
___ demi-	___ tetra-	6. ten
___ di-	___ tri-	7. one hundred
___ hemi-	___ semi-	8. one thousand
___ kilo-	___ uni-	9. half
___ mill-		10. one-tenth
		11. one-hundredth
		12. one-thousandth

B. Circle the correct meaning of each prefix or root below.

1. *Ambi* in *ambidextrous* means   **one   both   none**.
2. *Bene* in *beneficial* means   **good   bad   busy**.
3. *Circum* in *circumference* means   **on top   around   beside**.
4. *Com* in *companion* means   **good   through   together**.
5. *Con* in *congregrate* means   **around   together   good**.
6. *Cred* in *incredible* means   **to see   to say   to believe**.
7. *De* in *descend* means   **up   down   through**.
8. *Dis* in *disrespectful* means   **not   very   almost**.
9. *Ex* in *expel* means   **in   out   up**.
10. *Hydr* in *dehydrate* means   **air   water   land**.
11. *Ject* in *eject* means   **to fly   to jump   to throw**.
12. *Mal* in *malevolent* means   **good   bad   sick**.
13. *Mis* in *misguided* means   **wrongly   thoroughly   correctly**.
14. *Non* in *nonflammable* means   **very   somewhat   not**.
15. *Omni* in *omnipresent* means   **all   around   on top**.
16. *Poly* in *polysyllabic* means   **round   ten   many**.
17. *Port* in *export* means   **to throw   to sell   to carry**.
18. *Prim* in *primary* means   **easy   proper   first**.
19. *Retro* in *retroactive* means   **not   back   forward**.
20. *Rupt* in *interrupt* means   **to break   to carry   to talk**.
21. *Sur* in *surpass* means   **together   under   above**.
22. *Therm* in *thermostat* means   **air   cold   heat**

mono-, uni-   one

monogram	a design of two or more letters, such as initials, entwined into one (from Greek *gramma,* "letter")
monopoly	exclusive control by one group of people (from Greek *polein,* "to sell")
monorail	a railway with cars running on a single track (from Latin *regula,* "rod, straight piece of wood")
monotony	sameness; lack of variety (from Greek *tonos,* "tone")
unicorn	a mythical horselike animal with one horn (from Latin *cornu,* "horn")
unicycle	a vehicle with one wheel (from Greek *kuklos,* "circle, wheel")
unilateral	of, on, or by one side only (from Latin *latus,* "side")
unison	speaking or singing together (from Latin *sonus,* "sound")

Name _____

mono-, uni-

A. Fill in the blanks with words from the word list.

   1. It took many hours of practice before Mike could ride the _____ without falling.

   2. To distinguish between the sweaters we gave the twins for Christmas, we had _____ (s) put on them.

   3. The class recited the pledge of allegiance in _____ .

   4. After the fourth time he told the story, I was bored by the _____ .

   5. Without any prompting from her parents, Sasha made a _____ decision that she would clean up her room.

B. Circle the prefix that means "one" in each of the words below. Then use a dictionary to write the definition of each word.

   1. monocle _____

   2. uniform (adjective) _____

   3. universe _____

   4. monochrome (noun) _____

   5. unify _____

C. Do the following activities on separate sheets of paper.

   1. Design a monogram with the initials of your first, middle, and last names.
   2. Write a paragraph describing what you would do if you found a real live unicorn.

Wordstrength © 1989

biceps	any muscle having two points of origin (from Latin *caput,* "head")
bilingual	able to use two languages equally well (from Latin *lingua,* "tongue")
biped	a two-footed animal (from Latin *ped,* "foot")
bisect	divide into two (usually equal) parts (from Latin *sectus,* "cut")
dichromatic	having two colors (from Greek *khroma,* "color")
dilemma	a situation requiring a choice between two equal alternatives (from Greek *lemma,* "proposition")
diploma	a certificate awarded when a student has successfully completed a particular course of study (from Greek *ploos,* "-fold")
dipterous	having two wings (from Greek *pteron,* "wing, feather")

Wordstrength © 1989

bi-, di-

A. From the word list, select a word to complete each sentence. Write the word in the blank.

1. A fly is a _____ insect.

2. Lorenzo was taking a course in weight training, and would proudly flex his _____ when anyone asked how he was progressing.

3. Charlotte faced the _____ of whether to go to the movie with her friends or take the baby-sitting job.

4. Silvia is _____ because she speaks Spanish at home and English at school.

5. The geometry teacher told the students to _____ the circle.

B. The prefix *bi-* is often used in words about periods of time. Fill in the blanks in the following sentences with *bi-* words.

1. *Annual* means once a year. _____ means twice a year.

2. A *biennium* is a two-year period. _____ means once every two years.

3. *Centum* is the Latin word for one hundred. _____ means once every two hundred years.

4. A _____ event happens twice a month.

5. A _____ event happens twice a week.

C. Do the following on separate sheets of paper.

1. Draw a bicolored biped facing a dilemma.

2. Write a paragraph describing some jobs you could do if you were bilingual.

Wordstrength © 1989

tri-   three

triceratops

a dinosaur with a long horn above each eye, a short horn on the nose, and a large bony plate over the neck

(from Greek *keras*, "horn" + *ops*, "eye")

tricorn

a hat with three sides of the brim turned up

(from Latin *cornu*, "horn")

triennial

happening once every three years

(from Latin *annus*, "year")

triplicate

made in three copies

(from Latin *-plus*, "-fold")

quadr-, tetr-   four

quadrangle

a square open area surrounded by buildings

(from Latin *angulus*, "angle")

quadruped

an animal with four feet

(from Latin *ped*, "foot")

tetrachloride

a chemical compound containing four chlorine atoms per molecule

(from Greek *khloros*, "greenish yellow" + French *-ide*, a suffix indicating a chemical compound)

tetrahedron

a solid or hollow body with four triangular faces; a triangular pyramid

(from Greek *hedra*, "face")

tri-, quadr-, tetra-

A. Fill in the blank with the appropriate word from the word list.

1. The colonist wore a _____ to the Sons of Liberty meeting.

2. A common chemical used by dry cleaners is carbon _____ .

3. The insurance company asked for the accident report in _____ .

4. The simplest crystal sold in the gem and mineral store was in the shape of a

   _____ .

5. Every hour the _____ briefly fills with students rushing to their next class.

B. Using the origin of the root word, match each *tri-* or *quadr-* word to its definition.

____ 1. trivia (Latin, "place where three roads—*via*—meet")

____ 2. trigonometry (Greek *trigonon*, "triangle" + *metron*, "measure")

____ 3. quadriplegia (Greek *plege*, "a stroke")

____ 4. trifoliate (Latin *folium*, "leaf")

____ 5. quadripartite (Latin *pars*, "part")

____ 6. quadrilateral (Latin *latus*, "side")

A. paralysis of both arms and both legs
B. having four sides
C. a branch of mathematics concerned with the relationship between angles and sides of triangles and other figures
D. unimportant matters
E. having three leaves
F. divided into four parts, or having four participants

C. Draw and name the following figures on a separate sheet of paper:

1. a trilateral figure with three equal sides
2. a quadrilateral figure with four equal sides and four right angles
3. a quadrilateral figure with four right angles and whose adjacent sides are of different lengths

pentacle

a five-pointed star

(from Greek *-culum*, a diminutive suffix)

pentagon

a figure having five sides and five angles

(from Greek *gonia*, "angle")

pentameter

a line of verse containing five metrical feet or measures

(from Greek *metron*, "measure, meter")

pentathlon

a contest in which athletes try for the highest total score

(from Greek *athlon*, "contest")

quintessence

the purest or most typical example

(from Latin *quinta essentia*, "fifth essence," which medieval philosophers believed was the substance of which heavenly bodies were made)

quintet

a group of five musicians, or any group of five people or things

(from Latin *quintus*, "fifth")

quintuplet

any of five offspring born at one birth

(from Latin *-plex*, "-fold")

penta-, quint-

A. From the word list, select the word that best completes each sentence. Write the word in the blank.

1. Sheila thought that Herbie was the _____ of cuteness.

2. "He jests / at scars / who nev/er felt / a wound" is an example of a line of verse in

   _____ .

3. To be a _____ , the four musicians needed another guitar player.

4. In the Olympics, the _____ consists of a 5000-meter cross-country horseback ride, a 4000-meter cross-country run, a 300-meter swim, foil fencing, and pistol shooting.

5. There are _____ (s) and stripes on our nation's flag.

B. The prefixes for the numbers 6, 7, 8, and 9 are less frequently used than the prefixes for 1 through 5. Look in the dictionary to find a word using each of the following prefixes. (Hint: you can use names of geometrical shapes or of months.)

	Greek		Latin	
six	*hexa-*	_____	*ses-, sex-*	_____
seven	*hepta-*	_____	*sep-, sept-*	_____
eight	*oct-*	_____	*oct-*	_____
nine	*ennea-*	_____	*non-, novem-*	_____

C. Do the following on separate sheets of paper.

1. Draw a pentacle inside a pentagon.
2. In a paragraph describe the quintessential student or athlete or musician—or any other type of person you choose.

deca-   ten

decade
: a period of ten years
      (from Greek *deka*, "ten")

decagon
: a figure with ten sides and ten angles
      (from Greek *gonia*, "angle")

decathlon
: an athletic contest in which each contestant participates in ten events
      (from Greek *athlon*, "contest")

deci-   tenth

decibel
: a unit of sound intensity (technically, one-tenth of the common logarithm of the ratio between the power of two acoustic or electric signals)
      (from *bel*, a unit used in physics to compare ratios of power, named for Alexander Graham Bell)

deciliter
: a metric measure of volume equal to one-tenth of a liter
      (from Greek *litra*, "a pound")

decimal
: a fraction with an unwritten denominator of ten, indicated by a decimal point before the numerator
      (from Latin *decimus*, "tenth")

decimate
: to kill or destroy a large part of (originally, to kill every tenth person)
      (from Latin *decimus*, "tenth")

deca-, deci-

A. Fill in each blank with a word from the word list.

1. In the Middle Ages, the Black Plague _____ (ed) the population of Europe.

2. To win a _____ , you must excel at ten different sports.

3. The _____ level of the jackhammer hurt my ears.

4. Rhonda can recite the numerical value of pi to the tenth _____ .

5. My uncle is 50, so he has lived through five _____ (s).

B. A gram is .035 ounce. A liter is 1.057 quarts. A meter is 39.37 inches. Match each metric measure below with the item most nearly its size.

____1. decimeter   A. the amount of water a bathroom sink holds
____2. decameter   B. the length of a crayon
____3. decagram   C. the weight of a marble
____4. decigram   D. the length of a volleyball net
____5. decaliter   E. the weight of a straight pin
____6. deciliter   F. the amount of water a small glass holds

C. Do the following activities on separate sheets of paper.

1. Name five important events in the first decade of your life.
2. Use an encyclopedia or an almanac to compare the decibel levels of a whisper, a jet plane, and rock music. At what level is sound considered painful?

demi-, hemi-, semi-   half

demigod   a being who is part god and part human
                   (from Old English *god*, "god")

demitasse   a small coffee cup
                   (from French *tasse*, "cup")

hemisphere   half a spherical object, such as the earth
                   (from Greek *sphaia*, "small ball or globe")

semiannual   occurring half-yearly, or twice a year
                   (from Latin *annus*, "year")

semicolon   a punctuation mark (;) indicating more separation than a comma
                   and less separation than a period
                   (from Greek *kolon*, a unit of verse in Greek or Latin poetry)

semiconscious half-aware; half-awake
                   (from Latin *conscius*, "knowing with others")

demi-, hemi-, semi-

A. Fill in each blank with a word from the word list.

1. Miss O'Henry liked to drink her coffee out of a _____ because it was so dainty.

2. A _____ can be used to connect two independent clauses.

3. North and South America are in the Western _____ .

4. The store was holding its _____ sale.

5. In Greek mythology, Hercules was a _____ because he was the son of the god Zeus and a mortal woman.

B. Circle the words in which *semi* is used as a prefix meaning half.

seminar	semiformal	Seminole
semiliquid	semidetached	semimonthly
seminal	semiology	semiopaque

C. 1. On another sheet of paper, draw a picture that includes a large semicircle that covers the entire page, a person who is semiconscious and is wearing a semiformal outfit, a piece of furniture with a semidetached leg, and a semiopaque window.

2. Fill in the two blanks below with a synonym that uses prefixes meaning half. Use the dictionary to check your answers. Then draw and label each note on a separate sheet of paper.

quaver	eighth note	demisemiquaver	thirty-second note
_____	sixteenth note	_____	sixty-fourth note

Wordstrength © 1989

cent-   hundred

centennial   occurring once every one hundred years; a celebration of a
                hundredth anniversary
                   (from Latin *annus,* "year")

centipede   a long, many-segmented insect with a pair of legs on each segment
                   (from Latin *pes,* "foot")

centuple   to multiply by one hundred
                   (from Latin *-plus,* "-fold")

centurion   an officer commanding a unit of one hundred men in the Roman
                army
                   (from Latin *centum,* "hundred")

centi-   hundredth

centigrade   divided into one hundred degrees
                   (from Latin *gradus,* "stepping, going")

centimeter   a metric unit of length equal to one hundredth of a meter
                   (from Greek *metron,* "measure, meter")

cent-, centi-

A. Fill in each blank with a word from the word list.

1. In France, a _____ thermometer is used to measure temperature.

2. Our town was founded in 1887; we celebrated its _____ in 1987.

3. A _____ is a little over a third of an inch.

4. The normal _____ has only 35 pairs of legs.

5. To find out how many pennies you would get in exchange for a $10 bill, you would _____ ten.

B. The metric system uses the Greek prefix *hecto-* for 100, and the Latin prefix *centi-* for one hundredth. Match the following metric units of measurement with their equivalents. Put the number of the equivalent in the blank by the metric unit.

____ centigram   1. .021 pint

____ centiliter   2. 109.36 yards

____ centimeter   3. 26.4 gallons

____ hectogram   4. 3.527 ounces

____ hectoliter   5. .003 ounce

____ hectometer   6. .39 inch

C. Do the following activities on separate sheets of paper.

1. Use an almanac or other historical reference book to name three historical events for which this is a centennial year. You might choose the discovery or invention of something, the birth date of a famous person, or any other important event. Pick one event and describe in a paragraph how its centennial might be celebrated.

2. Draw a centipede. Measure its length in centimeters.

Wordstrength © 1989

kilo-, mill-　　　thousand

kilobyte　　　a unit of capacity equal to 1,024 bytes, which are groups of binary numbers processed as units by a computer

（perhaps from "bite"）

kilohertz　　　a unit of frequency equal to 1,000 cycles per second

（from *hertz,* named for Heinrich Hertz, a German physicist）

kilometer　　　a metric unit of length equal to 1,000 meters

（from Greek *metron,* "measure, meter"）

kilowatt　　　a unit of electrical power equal to 1,000 watts

（from *watt,* for James Watt, a Scottish engineer and inventor）

millenium　　　a period of a thousand years; a hoped-for period of great happiness, peace, and prosperity

（from Latin *annus,* "year"）

millipede　　　a long, many-segmented insect with two pairs of legs on each segment

（from Latin *pes,* "foot"）

milli-　　　thousandth

milligram　　　a metric measure of weight equal to one thousandth of a gram

（from Latin *gramma,* a small unit）

millimicron　　　a metric measure of length equal to one thousandth of a micron, or one millionth of a millimeter

（from Greek *mikros,* "small"）

Wordstrength © 1989

kilo-, mill-, milli-

A. Match each unit of measure with the item most nearly the same size. Put the number of the item in the blank by the unit of measure.

____ milligram	1. the length of an airport runway
____ kiloliter	2. the weight of a pair of shoes
____ kilometer	3. the weight of a grain of sand
____ milliliter	4. the thickness of a dime
____ kilogram	5. the volume of water in a swimming pool
____ millimeter	6. the volume of water in a raindrop

B. Write a synonym for each phrase, using a *milli-* or *kilo-* prefix.

1. a thousandth of a second _____

2. a hundred decagrams _____

3. a thousandth of a liter _____

4. a tenth of a centimeter _____

5. a thousand tons _____

6. a tenth of a centigram _____

C. 1. What is the frequency in kilohertz of your favorite radio station?_____
What is the frequency in megahertz (mega = million)? _____
How many kilowatt-hours of electricity were used in your home last month? (The monthly bill from the electric company gives this information.) _____

2. On a separate sheet of paper, draw a millipede. How many millimeters long is it?

Review Test 1

A. What would happen if we switched our language to the metric system? We might, for instance, call a small person a "demisemiliter" instead of a "half pint." Translate the following words and phrases into metrics by adding the correct prefix. Refer to a dictionary for U.S. and metric equivalents.

1. An inchworm would be a _____ meterworm.

2. The ten-yard line on a football field would be the _____ meter line.

3. A yardstick would be a _____ meterstick.

4. A peck of trouble would be a _____ liter of trouble.

5. A bushelbasket would be a _____ literbasket.

6. A poundcake would be a _____ gramcake.

7. A ten-gallon hat would be a four- _____ liter hat.

8. The saying "to walk a country mile" would be "to walk a country _____ meter."

9. The saying "an ounce of prevention is worth a pound of cure" would be "a _____ gram of prevention is worth a _____ gram of cure."

B. Fill in the blanks in this table of numbers.

Name	# of groups of 3 zeros after 1,000	Number
million	_____	1,000,000
_____	2	1,000,000,000
trillion	_____	_____
_____	_____	_____
_____	_____	_____
_____	_____	_____
_____	_____	_____
_____	_____	_____
_____	_____	_____

C. Label the pictures with words using number prefixes.

1. a _____
    insect

2. _____

3. _____

4. _____

5. _____

6. _____

7. _____

8. _____

9. _____

10. _____

11. _____

12. _____

ambi-, amphi-   both, around

ambiance
an environment or atmosphere
(from Latin *ire,* "to go")

ambidextrous
able to use both hands equally well
(from Latin *dexter,* "right hand")

ambiguous
having two or more possible meanings; indefinite, puzzling
(from Latin *ambigere,* "to wander," from Latin *agere,* "to do")

ambivalent
having opposite and conflicting feelings about something; unsure
(from Latin *valentia,* "worth, value")

amphibian
an animal with a backbone that is able to live on land and in water, such as a frog or a toad
(from Greek *bios,* "life")

amphitheater
an open space surrounded by rising rows of seats, such as a theater gallery or sports arena
(from Greek *theasthai,* "to see, to view")

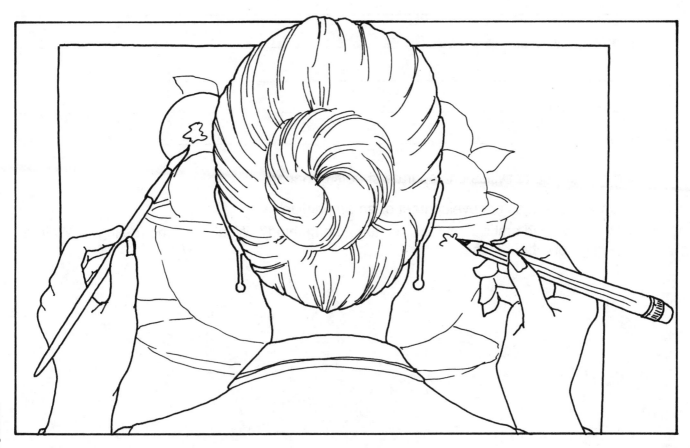

Name _____

ambi-, amphi-

A. Fill in each blank with a word from the word list.

1. When my brother broke his right wrist, he was still able to function fairly well because he is _____ .

2. _____ (s) begin their lives as tadpoles.

3. Janie Sue felt _____ about Jordie's invitation to the school dance.

4. Alex was getting frustrated because the directions for the model airplane were poorly written and _____ .

5. The elegant _____ of her friend's home always made Donna feel awkward.

B. After each word below, write its part of speech and a brief definition.

1. ambidexterity _____

_____

2. ambivalence _____

_____

3. ambiguity _____

_____

4. amphibious _____

_____

C. Do the following activities on separate sheets of paper.

1. Draw the stages of development of an amphibian.
2. Have you had ambivalent feelings about something? What were the feelings? Write a paragraph about them.

ben, bene   good, well

benediction

a blessing

(from Latin *dicere,* "to speak")

benefactor

a person who gives help or support, especially financial aid

(from Latin *facere,* "to do")

beneficial

having a good or helpful effect

(from Latin *facere,* "to do")

beneficiary

a person who receives a benefit or advantage, such as an inheritance

(from Latin *facere,* "to do")

benevolent

doing good things; being good-hearted, kind

(from Latin *volens,* "wishing")

benign

gentle and kind; not threatening life

(from Latin *genus,* "born")

ben, bene

A. Fill in each blank with a word from the word list.

1. The musician needed a _____ to support him financially.

2. The priest said the _____ after the mass.

3. It is _____ to study vocabulary before taking a standardized test.

4. The _____ of his life insurance policy would receive $25,000.

5. My grandmother was very relieved when the tests showed that the tumor was

   _____ .

B. Circle each word below in which *ben* or *bene* is used as a prefix meaning "good, well."

beneath	Benelux
Benedict	benighted
benefaction	benignant
beneficence	benumb
benefit	benzene

C. Do the following activities on separate sheets of paper.

1. Draw an outdoor scene in benign weather.
2. List five things that are beneficial to your health.

Wordstrength © 1989

circa
about or approximately
(from Latin *circa,* "about")

circuitous
roundabout; indirect; devious
(from Latin *ire,* "to go")

circulation
the act of moving in a circle or circuit or of moving from place to place
(from Latin *circularis,* "round")

circumference
the outer line of a circle; the length of this line
(from Latin *ferre,* "to carry")

circumnavigate
to sail around something, especially the world
(from Latin *navigare,* "to sail")

circumscribe
to draw or form a line around, especially a circle; to limit or restrain
(from Latin *scribere,* "to write, draw")

circumspect
careful to consider all related circumstances before acting or deciding; cautious
(from Latin *specere,* "to look")

circumvent
to avoid or find a way around
(from Latin *venire,* "to come")

Name _____

circ-, circum-

A. Fill in each blank with a word from the word list.

1. Johnny came up with some very creative excuses to _____ doing his homework.

2. Ferdinand Magellan's ship was the first to _____ the world.

3. On her first day at the new school, Marie was _____ ; she wanted to get a sense of the various crowds before she picked new friends.

4. When his parents said he could never stay out past nine o'clock, Arthur felt he was being unreasonably _____ (d).

5. The doctor said that my grandmother must find some type of exercise that would help improve the _____ of her blood.

B. Look up the following words in a dictionary. Briefly define each word in the blank that follows it.

1. circadian _____

2. circuitry _____

3. circumflex _____

4. circumlocution _____

5. circumstantial _____

C. 1. On the map below, draw a line to show a route that could be used to circumnavigate Africa.

2. On a separate sheet of paper, define the following terms: circulating library, circuit rider, circuit breaker, circuit court.

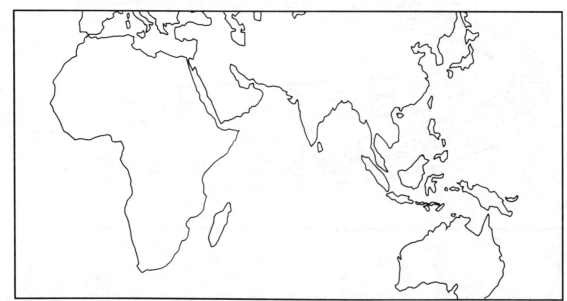

30

com-   together, with

combat
: to fight with; to struggle against, especially to try to reduce or eliminate
  (from Latin *battuere,* "to beat")

commiserate
: to express sorrow or pity
  (from Latin *miserari,* "to pity")

companion
: a person who accompanies or associates with another
  (from Latin *panis,* "bread, food")

compare
: to note the similarities or differences of
  (from Latin *par,* "equal")

compete
: to try to outdo or defeat someone else
  (from Latin *petere,* "to seek, strive")

compose
: to form by putting together
  (from Latin *pausare,* "to place")

compound
: something made of several parts
  (from Latin *ponere,* "to put")

compress
: to squeeze together; to reduce in size or volume
  (from Latin *premere,* "to press")

com-

A. Fill in each blank with a word from the word list.

1. The scientists are doing research to find a way to _____ the new disease.

2. My grandmother has been very lonely since my grandfather died, so my mother hired a woman to be her _____.

3. Green paint can be made from a _____ of blue and yellow paint.

4. The two classes _____ (d) against each other in a baseball game.

5. For geometry class, John will _____ the diameters of a volleyball and a basketball.

B. Match each word with its origin. Then circle the words in the first column that use *com-* as a prefix meaning "together, with."

_____ compel   1. *complexus,* "entwined, braided together"

_____ complicate   2. *compartiri,* "to share with, divide"

_____ coma   3. *compromittere,* "to promise together"

_____ compartment   4. *komoidos,* "a singer in the festivities"

_____ comedy   5. *compellere,* "to drive (cattle) together"

_____ complex   6. *(aster) kometes,* "long-haired star"

_____ compromise   7. *complicare,* "folded together"

_____ comet   8. *koma,* "deep sleep"

C. Do the following activities on separate sheets of paper.

1. Draw a picture that compares combat and competition.
2. You have just been chosen to take a trip into space. One person can travel with you. Whom would you choose to be your companion? Write a paragraph explaining why.

Wordstrength © 1989

con-   together, with

conform   to act in agreement with rules, customs, standards
           (from Latin *formare,* "to shape")

congregate   to come together in a group; to assemble
           (from Latin *gregare,* "to flock")

conjunction   the state of being joined; combination
           (from Latin *jungere,* "to join")

connect   to join
           (from Latin *nectere,* "to bind, tie")

consent   to agree or give permission
           (from Latin *sentire,* "to feel")

construct   to make or put together by assembling parts
           (from Latin *struere,* "to pile up")

contend   to fight; to compete; to argue
           (from Latin *tendere,* "to strain, stretch")

convenient   suited to one's comfort, needs, or purpose
           (from Latin *venire,* "to come")

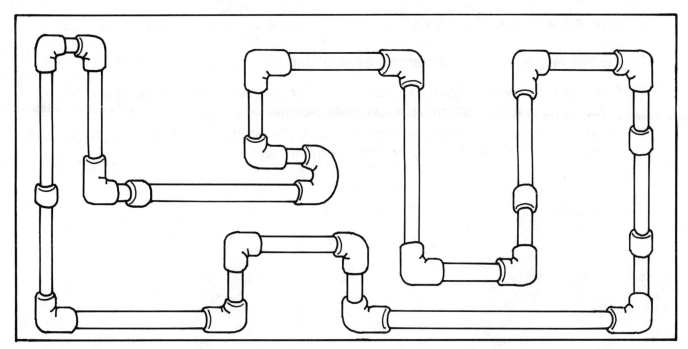

Name _____

con-

A. Find the opposite of each of the following words in the words list and write it in the blank.

1. destroy _____

2. sever _____

3. forbid _____

4. agree _____

5. disperse _____

6. annoying _____

7. separation _____

B. Use the root of each *con-* word to help you briefly define each word. Refer to a dictionary to check your definitions.

1. configuration (*figura,* "shape") _____

2. consequence (*sequi,* "to follow") _____

3. conspire (*spirare,* "to breathe") _____

4. congeal (*gelare,* "to freeze") _____

5. contagious (*tangere,* "to touch") _____

6. content *(noun)* (*tenere,* "to hold") _____

7. consensus (*sentire,* "to feel") _____

C. Do the following activities on separate sheets of paper.

1. Draw a person who conforms with the style of dress in your school. Draw another person who is a nonconformist. Color both pictures.

2. Write a paragraph describing the conformist. Write another paragraph describing the nonconformist. Circle the conjunctions in both paragraphs.

cred   to believe

accredit   to give credit for; to authorize or recognize officially
                (from French à, "to")

credence   acceptance or belief
                (from Latin *credere*, "to trust, believe")

credential   letter or document that proves or affirms a person's identity or right
                to hold a certain position
                (from Latin *credere*, "to trust, believe")

credo   a set of beliefs or opinions
                (from Latin *credere*, "to trust, believe")

credulous   inclined to believe anything, often without sufficient proof
                (from Latin *credere*, "to trust, believe")

discredit   to reject as untrue; to cast doubt on; to disgrace
                (from Latin *dis*, "not")

incredible   unbelievable
                (from Latin *in-*, "not")

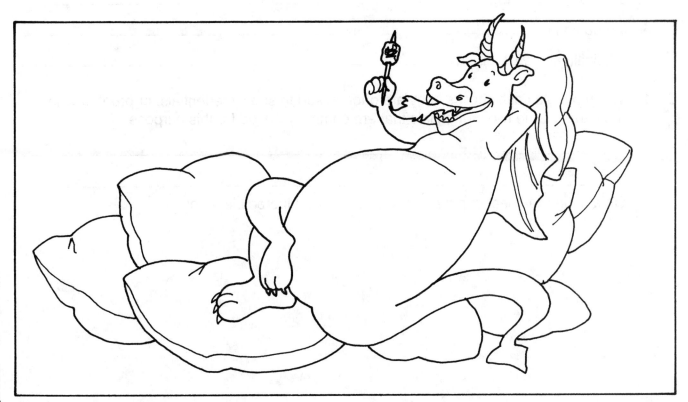

Wordstrength © 1989

Name _____

cred

A. Fill in each blank with a word from the word list.

1. His explanation for not having his homework was truly _____.

2. The golden rule is an important part of my _____.

3. Five years of college study are usually required to obtain a teaching _____.

4. Because they knew that enrollment had been dropping, they gave _____ to the rumor that the school would soon close.

5. Little Mikey was still _____; he would believe anything his big brothers told him.

6. The candidate's staff was trying hard to find ways to _____ the opponent.

B. Look up the following words and phrases in a dictionary and write a brief definition for each.

1. on credit _____

2. to one's credit _____

3. creditor _____

4. incredulous _____

5. credibility _____

C. 1. When people cash checks, they are often asked to show credentials, or proof of who they are. Name two credentials that are commonly used for this purpose.

_____

_____

2. On a separate sheet of paper, draw and color an incredible monster.

de-   away, down

debase

to lower in quality, rank, or dignity
   (from Latin *basis,* "base, pedestal")

decline

a downward slope *(noun)*; to refuse politely, to turn down *(verb)*
   (from Latin *clinare,* "to bend")

deduct

to subtract or take away from a total amount
   (from Latin *ducere,* "to lead")

deflate

to release air or gas from a container; to reduce the confidence or certainty of
   (from Latin *flare,* "to blow")

deposit

to put or lay down; to put away for safekeeping
   (from Latin *ponere,* "to put")

descend

to go down; to come down from
   (from Latin *scandere,* "to climb")

desultory

moving or jumping from one thing to another in an aimless way; disconnected or random
   (from Latin *salire,* "to jump")

detrimental

damaging or harmful
   (from Latin *terere,* "to rub")

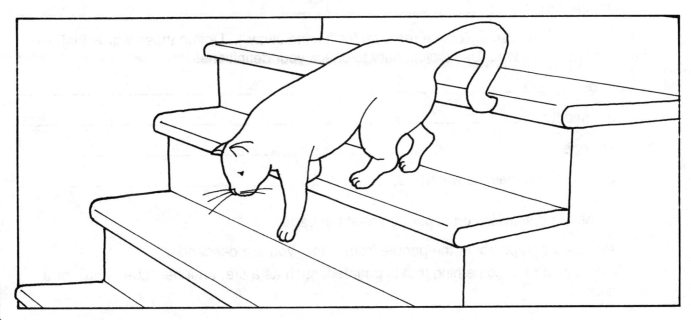

Name _____

---

de-

A. Fill in each blank with a word from the word list.

1. Hilda plans to _____ the money she earns this summer in a savings account.

2. He was so self-confident that no amount of criticism could_____ his ego.

3. I had the feeling that Joanie's mind was elsewhere, because her conversation was so _____.

4. Toxic chemicals are _____ to the environment.

5. She tactfully _____(d) his request to loan him her notes of the class lectures.

6. When he saw the bear, he quickly turned around and began to _____ the mountain.

B. 1. The prefix *de-* can indicate a reversal (or a "turning away" in the opposite direction). Define these words that use *de-* to mean a reversal. Use a dictionary to check your definitions.

   deactivate _____

   debrief _____

   decode _____

   desegregate _____

2. The prefix *de-* can also indicate a removal (or "taking away"). Define these words that use *de-* to mean a removal. Use a dictionary to check your definitions.

   defrost _____

   dehumidify _____

   dethrone _____

   dehydrate (*hydr* means water) _____

C. Do the following activities on separate sheets of paper.

1. Write a paragraph about the people from whom you are descended.
2. Draw a picture of something that is deflated, such as a tire, an inner tube, a ball, or a balloon.

disadvantage	an unfavorable condition or circumstance (from Latin *abante*, "before" + *-atus*, a suffix meaning "the condition of being")
disequilibrium	loss or lack of stability or balance (from Latin *aequus*, "equal" + *libra*, "balance")
dishonor	loss of respect or reputation; disgrace (from Latin *honor*, "honor")
disparity	a lack of equality or similarity (from Latin *paritas*, "equality")
disrespectful	impolite, rude (from Latin *re-*, "back" + *specere*, "to look")
dissatisfied	not pleased; not content (from Latin *satis*, "enough" + *facere*, "to make")
dissimilar	unlike or different (from Latin *similis*, "like")

Wordstrength © 1989

dis-

A. From the word list, select a synonym for each of the following words or phrases. Write the synonym in the blank beside each word.

1. dizziness _____

2. difference _____

3. not the same _____

4. handicap _____

5. bad-mannered _____

6. displeased _____

B. The prefix *dis-* is also used to reverse the meaning of the root. The following words are examples. Guess the meaning of each word from its root. Then check your answers in a dictionary.

1. disarm (*dis-* + *arma,* "tools, weapons") _____
   (guess)

   _____
   (definition)

2. disburse (*dis-* + *bursa,* "purse") _____
   (guess)

   _____
   (definition)

3. disclose (*dis-* + *clausus,* "closed") _____
   (guess)

   _____
   (definition)

4. discount (*dis-* + *computare,* "to add") _____
   (guess)

   _____
   (definition)

C. Do the following activities on separate sheets of paper.

1. Draw a picture containing four dissimilar objects.
2. Write a paragraph about a situation in which you were at a disadvantage.

ex-	**out, out of**

excavate

to make a hole in; to uncover by digging

(from Latin *cavare,* "to hollow")

excerpt

a passage taken from a book, article, speech, or other piece of writing

(from Latin *carpere,* "to pick, pluck")

exorbitant

too great, too extreme

(from Latin *orbita,* "route, orbit")

exotic

foreign or introduced from another country; strikingly different

(from Latin and Greek *ex-,* "out")

expel

to force or drive out; to dismiss from school or society by official decision

(from Latin *pellere,* "to drive")

extinguish

to put out; to bring to an end

(from Latin *stinguere,* "to quench, put out")

extrude

to force or push out; to shape metal or plastic by forcing through a die

(from Latin *trudere,* "to thrust")

exude

to ooze; to discharge gradually

(from Latin *sudare,* "to sweat, ooze")

Name _____

_____

A. A word from the word list can be substituted for each underlined phrase in the sentences below. Write the word in the blank after each sentence.

1. She dreamed of travel to some faraway <u>foreign and unusual</u> place.

   _____

2. The firefighters worked for five days trying to <u>put out</u> the forest fire.

   _____

3. He <u>oozed</u> confidence. _____ (d)

4. The team of archaelogists <u>uncovered by digging</u> an ancient royal tomb high in the Andes. _____ (d)

5. The prices in that store are <u>too great</u>. _____

6. The principal said that if there were any more incidents, he would <u>officially dismiss</u> the boy <u>from school</u>. _____

B. In many words, the prefix *ex-* has been shortened to *e-* because it sounds better. For instance, we say "emerge" instead of "exmerge," and "event" instead of "exvent." Use a dictionary to find the meanings of the following words that use *e-* instead of *ex-*.

1. eclipse _____

2. eject _____

3. elicit _____

4. emigrate _____

5. emit _____

6. erode _____

C. Do the following activities on separate sheets of paper.

1. Draw a picture that includes an excavation, an eclipse, and an exotic landscape.
2. Look up the following words in a dictionary. Use the origins of the words to compare and contrast the meanings of the words in each group.
   - *emigrant, exile, expatriate*
   - *excise, exercise, exorcise*

hydr, hydro   water

dehydrate
    to lose or remove water
        (from Latin *de-* "away from")

hydrant
    a large, upright pipe connected to a water main
        (from Greek *hydor,* "water")

hydraulics
    being operated by or using a liquid
        (from Greek *hydraulis,* "water organ or tube")

hydrocarbon
    any of a large class of organic compounds that contain only carbon and hydrogen
        (from Latin *carbo,* "coal")

hydroelectric
    of or relating to electricity produced by the energy of flowing water, such as that from a dam
        (from Latin *electricus,* "produced from amber by rubbing")

hydrophobia
    an abnormal fear of water; rabies
        (from Greek *phobos,* "fear")

hydroplane
    a light, fast boat designed to skim along the surface of water; a seaplane
        (from Latin *planus,* "level")

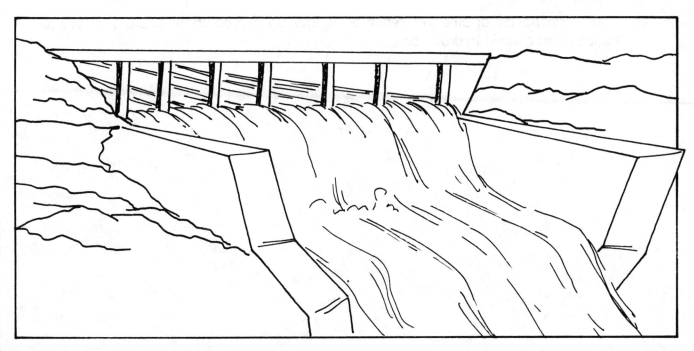

Name _____

hydr, hydro

A. Fill in each blank with a word from the word list.

1. We crossed the English Channel in a _____ .

2. To make raisins, you _____ grapes.

3. Hoover Dam is an important source of _____ power.

4. On extremely hot days, the mayor orders all _____ (s) to be opened so that people can cool off in the water.

5. Because it causes an inability to swallow liquids, rabies is also known as _____ .

B. Look up these *hydro* words in the dictionary. Write their meanings.

1. hydra _____

2. hydrogen _____

3. hydrolysis _____

4. hydroponics _____

5. hydrothermal _____

C. Do the following activities on separate sheets of paper.

1. Draw a hydroplane.
2. In an encyclopedia or other reference book, look up *hydrocarbon*. Make a list of substances that contain hydrocarbons.

ject   to throw

abject   contemptible; humble; wretched
                (from Latin *ab-,* "from")

conjecture   a guess or a judgment without sufficient evidence
                (from Latin *com-,* "together")

dejected   sad and depressed
                (from Latin *de-,* "down")

eject   to force out or cause to be removed
                (from Latin *e-,* "out")

interject   to break in with a comment while someone else is speaking
                (from Latin *inter-,* "between")

projectile   any object fired from a gun by means of an explosive charge, such as a bullet or shell; something thrown
                (from Latin *pro-,* "before, forward")

rejection   a refusal to accept or to use
                (from Latin *re-,* "back")

trajectory   the path, especially a curve, traced by a moving object
                (from Latin *trans-,* "across, over")

ject

A. Fill in each blank with a word from the word list.

1. The tornado turned trees and shingles into dangerous _____ (s).

2. He offered an _____ apology.

3. Just before the plane crashed, the pilot pushed the button that would _____ him.

4. The crowd followed the _____ of the ball as it sailed out of the ballpark.

5. His accusation was based only on _____ .

6. "I know the answer," she _____ (ed) before the game-show emcee could even finish asking the question.

B. Circle the root that means "to throw" in each of the following words. Then look up each word in a dictionary and briefly define it.

1. project (noun)   _____

   (verb)   _____

2. adjective   _____

3. injection   _____

4. reject (noun)   _____

   (verb)   _____

5. interjection   _____

6. object (noun)   _____

   (verb)   _____

7. subject (noun)   _____

   (verb)   _____

C. Do the following activities on separate sheets of paper.

1. Draw a picture that shows the trajectory of a projectile.

2. Write a paragraph about someone who is dejected. Describe why he or she is dejected and how he or she looks and behaves.

Review Test 2

A. Circle the new root or prefix in each of the following words. Then write the meaning of the root or prefix in the blank after the word.

1. excavate _____

2. benefactor _____

3. disrespectful _____

4. incredible _____

5. deflate _____

6. hydraulic _____

7. ambivalent _____

8. projectile _____

9. commiserate _____

10. circumference _____

11. congregate _____

B. Fill in each blank with the prefix or root that will make a word to fit the definition.

1. _____ base   to lower in quality, rank, or dignity

2. de _____ ate   to lose or remove water

3. _____ advantage   an unfavorable condition or circumstance

4. _____ dextrous   able to use both hands equally well

5. _____ cerpt   a passage taken from a book, article, or speech

6. _____ press   to squeeze together

7. _____ vent   to avoid or find a way around

8. _____ ject   to break in with a comment while someone else is speaking

9. _____ ficial   having a good or helpful effect

10. _____ junction   the state of being joined; combination

11. _____ ence   acceptance or belief

mal-   bad, wrongful

malady   a disorder or disease
                   (from Latin *male habitus,* "badly kept, out of condition")

malefactor   a criminal or wrongdoer
                   (from Latin *facere,* "to do")

malevolent   showing ill will or wishing harm to others
                   (from Latin *volens,* "wishing")

malice   a desire or intention to hurt or cause suffering
                   (from Latin *malus,* "bad")

malignant   feeling or showing extreme ill will; tending to cause death
                   (from Latin *genus,* "born")

malnourished   suffering from bad or inadequate nutrition
                   (from Latin *nutrire,* "to nourish")

malpractice   any improper conduct, especially by a person in an official or
                   professional position
                   (from Greek *prassein,* "to do")

mal-

A. Match the meanings with the words. Put the number of the definition beside the correct word.

   _____ malnourished

   _____ malefactor

   _____ malignant

   _____ malady

   _____ malevolent

   _____ malice

1. sickness
2. wishing harm to others
3. someone who breaks the law
4. a wish to hurt others
5. likely to cause death
6. starving

B. Look up the following *mal-* words in a dictionary and briefly define them in the blanks.

1. maladjusted _____

2. malcontent _____

3. malaise _____

4. malaria _____

5. malediction _____

6. malfunction _____

7. malinger _____

C. Do the following activities on separate sheets of paper.

1. Write a one- or two-page short story about a malefactor who maltreats another person. Include the following words in your story: *malice, malnourished, malevolent,* and *malignant.*

2. Draw a picture of malice.

mis-	**badly, wrongly**

miscalculate
: to figure out incorrectly; to make an error in counting
  (from Latin *calculus*, a small stone used in counting)

misconstrue
: to interpret wrongly; to misunderstand
  (from Latin *construere*, "to build")

misdeed
: a crime or wicked action
  (from Middle English *dede*, "deed")

misfit
: a person who is badly adjusted to his or her environment
  (from Middle English *fitten*, "arranged")

misguided
: foolish; misled
  (from Old Provençal *guida*, "to show the way")

misnomer
: a name wrongly applied to a person or a thing
  (from Latin *nomen*, "name")

misquote
: to quote incorrectly
  (from Latin *quotare*, "to mark the number of")

mistrial
: a trial declared invalid because of some error in the proceedings
  (from Old French *trier*, "to try")

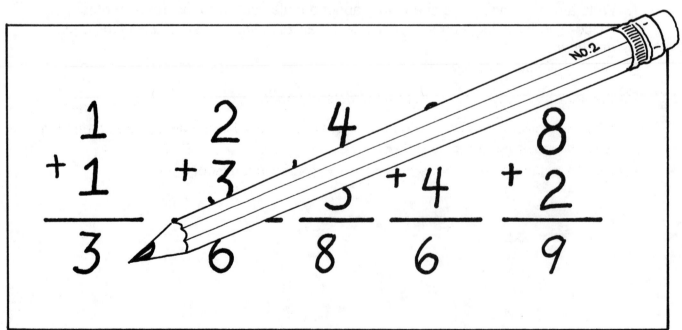

mis-

A. Fill in each blank with a word from the word list.

1. The teacher _____(d) Norman's silence; she thought it meant that he didn't know the answer.

2. Although the other members of the basketball team towered over "Shorty," the nickname was a _____ for this 6-foot, 2-inch athlete.

3. Her passion for opera made her a _____ among her classmates.

4. The clerk _____ (d) the sales tax on the sale.

5. The business executive claimed that the reporter had _____ (d) him.

6. Because evidence had been gathered illegally, the judge declared a

   _____ .

B. Define the following *mis-* words in the blanks beside them. Refer to a dictionary to check your answers.

1. misadventure _____

2. misconduct _____

3. misfortune _____

4. misinform _____

5. mislay _____

6. misprint _____

7. misrepresent _____

C. Do the following activities on separate sheets of paper.

1. Write a page about a time when a family member or a friend saw you do something and misconstrued the entire event.

2. Draw a picture of a misfit or of someone engaged in a misdeed.

nonchalant

appearing unconcerned; indifferent; cool
(from Latin *calere,* "to be warm")

noncommittal

not revealing one's position or purpose
(from Latin *committere,* "to bring together, entrust")

nonconformist

someone who does not always follow accepted attitudes or behavior
(from Latin *conformare,* "to have the same form")

nondescript

of no particular type; hard to describe
(from Latin *describere,* "to write down")

nonentity

a person or thing of no importance
(from Latin *entitas,* "being")

nonflammable

not easily set on fire
(from Latin *flammare,* "to blaze")

nonplus

to puzzle or bewilder so much that one cannot say or do anything
(from Latin *plus,* "more, further")

nonprofit

not intended to make money
(from Latin *profectus,* "progress, success")

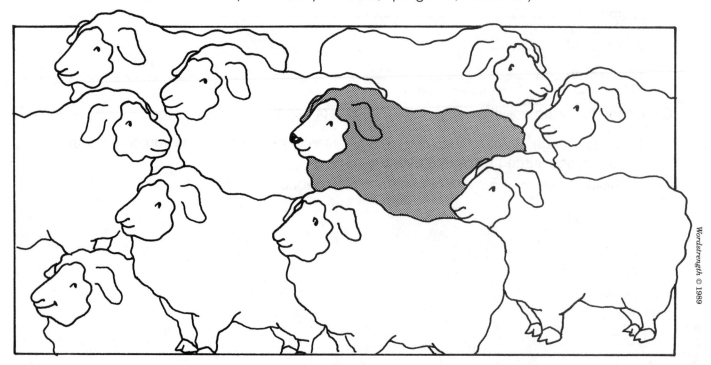

non-

A. Fill in each blank with a word from the word list.

1. We checked the Halloween costume for a tag that said _____ because there's always the chance of brushing too close to a jack-o'-lantern candle.

2. The Red Cross is a _____ organization because it doesn't make money from its aid to victims of war and natural disasters.

3. She always dressed with a lot of style and made the rest of us feel _____ and rather dull.

4. He had been a _____ since he was ten years old and insisted on taking bagpipe lessons.

5. When Nancy asked if she would get a pony for her birthday, her mother just smiled and remained _____ .

B. Briefly define the following *non-* words. Refer to a dictionary to check your answers.

1. nonfiction _____

2. nonstandard _____

3. nonverbal _____

4. nonviolent _____

5. nonrestrictive _____

C. Do the following activities on separate sheets of paper.

1. Draw three people: a conformist to today's fashions, a nonconformist, and someone who is nondescript.

2. Write a paragraph about nonplussing someone who is nonchalant.

omnibus — including many things or having a variety of purposes or uses *(adjective)*; a single book containing several works on a particular topic or by one author *(noun)*; bus *(noun)*

(from Latin *omnibus,* "for all")

omnifarious — of all varieties or forms

(from Latin *fari,* "to speak")

omnipotent — having great or unlimited power; all-powerful

(from Latin *potens,* "able")

omnipresent — present in all places at the same time
(from Latin *praesens,* "present")

omniscient — having unlimited knowledge

(from Latin *sciens,* "knowing")

omnivorous — eating both plants and animals as food
(from Latin *vorare,* "to devour")

omni-

A. Fill in each blank with a word from the word list.

1. Humans are _____ , although some people choose to be vegetarians.

2. When Howard was little, he believed his parents were _____ because they could always answer his questions.

3. Her perfume was so strong that its smell seemed almost _____ .

4. The junk shop contained an _____ selection of merchandise.

5. An _____ of the author's works was published last year.

B. Briefly define each of the following words. Refer to a dictionary to check your answers.

1. omnipotence _____

2. omnivore _____

3. omniscience _____

4. omnipresence _____

5. omnidirectional _____

C. Do the following activities on separate sheets of paper.

1. Write a short story about an omnipotent creature that is omniscient, omnipresent, and omnivorous. To prove that the creature is all of those things, give examples.

2. Draw a picture of an omnipotent, omniscient, omnipresent, omnivorous creature.

poly-   much, many

polychrome   having various or changing colors
(from Greek *chroma,* "color")

polyester   any of a large number of synthetic resins used in making plastics and fibers
(from German *essigäther,* "vinegar ether")

polyglot   a person who knows several different languages
(from Greek *glotta,* "the tongue")

polygon   a closed plane figure, especially one with more than four sides and angles
(from Greek *gonia,* "angle")

polygraph   an instrument that records many physiological reactions at once, such as heartbeat, breathing, and blood pressure, and is often used as a lie detector
(from Greek *graphein,* "to write, draw")

polyhedron   a solid or hollow body bounded by many plane faces
(from Greek *hedra,* "side, base, seat")

polysyllabic   having many syllables, especially four or more
(from Greek *syllabe,* "that which holds together")

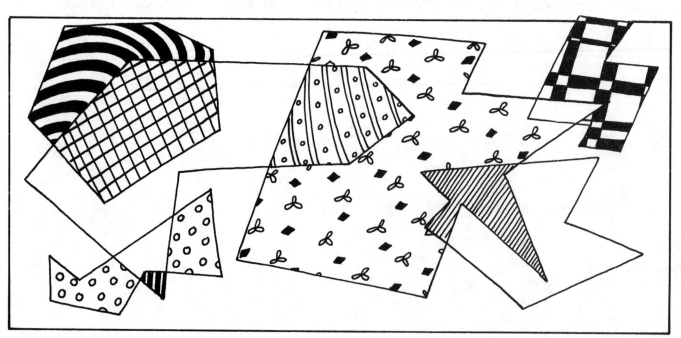

poly-

A. Fill in each blank with a word from the word list.

1. In general, clothes made of _____ are not considered stylish.

2. The view through a kaleidoscope is a _____ one.

3. A pentagon can also be called a _____ .

4. He offered to take a _____ test to show that he was telling the truth.

5. A person who speaks Spanish, French, Italian, Portuguese, and English is a

_____ .

B. Look up the following words in a dictionary and briefly define them.

1. polyandry _____

2. polygamy _____

3. polygyny _____

4. polyphonic _____

5. polyunsaturated _____

C. Do the following activities on separate sheets of paper.

1. List all the words on the word list that are not polysyllabic. Break each of those words into syllables.

2. Draw a polychrome picture of polygons.

port	**to bring, to carry**

comport — to conduct oneself, or to behave in a specified manner
(from Latin *com-,* "together")

deport — to expel from a country
(from Latin *de-,* "away")

export — to send goods to another country
(from Latin *ex-,* "out, out of")

import — to bring in from an outside source, especially from a foreign country
(from Latin *in-,* "in")

portfolio — a flat case for carrying papers, manuscripts, drawings, or other documents
(from Latin *folium,* "a leaf")

purport — to claim or imply, often falsely
(from Latin *pro-,* "forth")

rapport — a feeling of understanding or sympathy
(from Latin *re-,* "again")

Wordstrength © 1989

port

A. Fill in each blank with a word from the word list.

1. Gloria's grandmother urged her to _____ herself like a lady.

2. The artist kept her sketches in a leather _____ .

3. People without official immigration papers can be _____ (ed) to their home countries.

4. The twins had a special _____ .

5. The United States _____ (s) oil from the Middle East.

6. He announced that he had discovered what he _____ (ed) to be a cure for the common cold.

B. Circle the root that means "to bring, to carry" in each of the following words. Then briefly define each word in the blank that follows it. Check your definitions in a dictionary.

1. transportation _____

2. reporter _____

3. porter _____

4. supportive _____

5. portable _____

C. Do the following activities on separate sheets of paper.

1. Look around your classroom or your home and find ten things that are imported. (Look for "Made in _____ " on labels or stamped or printed on the objects.) List the ten items and the countries they come from.

2. Write a paragraph describing the rapport you have with a relative or a friend—or a pet.

primary

first; fundamental, basic

    (from Latin *primus,* "first")

primate

any mammal of the group *Primata* that includes humans, monkeys, and apes, and is characterized especially by flexible hands and feet, each with five digits

    (from Latin *primus,* "first")

prime

first in rank or importance *(adjective)*; the most perfect stage or condition *(noun)*; to prepare or make ready for a particular purpose *(verb)*

    (from Latin *primus,* "first")

primer

a simple book of instruction, especially for reading

    (from Latin *primus,* "first")

primeval

of or relating to prehistoric times

    (from Latin *aevum,* "an age")

primitive

being the earliest stage of something; crude, simple, rough, undeveloped

    (from Latin *primus,* "first")

primordial

being or happening first in time; original

    (from Latin *ordiri,* "to begin")

Wordstrength © 1989

prim

A. Fill in each blank with a word from the word list.

1. Dinosaurs are _____ creatures.

2. _____ school is followed by secondary school.

3. Gorillas, orangutans, chimpanzees, and baboons are all_____ (s).

4. The purpose of the coach's pep talk was to _____ the team for the game.

5. School books that are used to teach first-graders to read are sometimes called _____ (s).

6. When the storm caught us by surprise on our hiking trip, we built a _____ shelter of branches.

B. Look up the following phrases in a dictionary and briefly define them.

1. prime meridian _____

2. prime number _____

3. primary color _____

4. prime minister _____

5. prime time _____

6. prima donna _____

7. primary election _____

C. Do the following activities on separate sheets of paper.

1. List the prime numbers from 1 to 100.
2. Draw a globe with the prime meridian colored in red.

retro-   back, backward

retroactive   going into effect as of a specified date in the past
(from Latin *agere,* "to act")

retroflex   curved or turned backward
(from Latin *flexus,* "bent, curved")

retrograde   moving backward, especially to an earlier or less developed condition; retreating
(from Latin *gradus,* "step, rank, degree")

retrogress   to move backward, especially to an earlier or worse condition
(from Latin *gradus,* "step, rank, degree")

retrorocket   a small rocket on a spacecraft, fired in the direction in which the spacecraft is traveling, in order to slow it down
(from Italian *rocchetta,* "a short staff used in spinning")

retrospective   looking back into the past *(adjective)*; a representative exhibition of the lifetime work of an artist
(from Latin *specere,* "to look")

Name _____

retro-

A. Fill in each blank with a word from the word list.

1. If the child got out of his sickbed too soon, he might _____ .

2. According to the workers' new contract, their salary increases were

   _____ .

3. After the criminal went to jail, he became _____ about his life.

4. For a six-year-old, thumb-sucking is _____ behavior.

5. The astronaut fired the _____ when it was time to begin the descent
   back to earth.

B. Look up the following words in a dictionary and briefly define them.

1. retrofire _____

2. retrofit _____

3. retrogression _____

4. retrospection _____

C. Do the following activities on separate sheets of paper.

1. Take a retrospective look at your life. List five of its most important events.
2. Draw a picture of a retrorocket being fired on a spacecraft.

rupt	**to break, to burst**

abrupt   sudden or unexpected; discourteous or brief, especially in manner
         (from Latin *ab-,* "off")

bankruptcy   a legal declaration of the inability to pay one's debts; complete failure
         (from Italian *banca,* "table, moneylender's exchange table")

corrupt   dishonest, evil, or no longer innocent
         (from Latin *com-,* "together")

disrupt   to break up or throw into confusion
         (from Latin *dis-,* "apart")

erupt   to burst or force out violently
         (from Latin *e-,* "out")

interrupt   to break the continuity of; to hinder or stop by breaking in on
         (from Latin *inter-,* "between")

rupture   to break or burst
         (from Latin *ruptus,* "broken")

Wordstrength © 1989

rupt

A. Fill in each blank with a word from the word list.

1. Cries of "Fire!" _____ (ed) the audience.

2. With one hand over his mouth and the other clutching his stomach, he made an
_____ departure.

3. "We _____ this program to bring you an important news
announcement. "

4. The last volcano to _____ in the continental United States was Mt. St.
Helens.

5. Nothing could change his belief that all politicians are _____ .

6. Business had gotten so bad for the little grocery store that the owner had to declare
_____ .

7. They rushed him to the hospital with a _____ (d) appendix.

B. Briefly define the following words. In the parentheses, name their part of speech. Refer
to a dictionary to check your answers.

1. abruptly   (   ) _____

2. corruption (   ) _____

3. disruptive (   ) _____

4. eruption   (   ) _____

5. interruption (   ) _____

C. Do the following activities on separate sheets of paper.

1. Draw a picture of a volcano erupting.
2. List five ways to handle someone who constantly interrupts others when they are
speaking.

sur-	**above, over**

surcharge — an extra charge
    (from Latin *carricare,* "to load a wagon, cart")

surmount — to get over, across, or on top of
    (from Latin *montare,* "to go uphill")

surname — family name
    (from Latin *nomen,* "name")

surpass — to be better or greater than
    (from French *passer,* "to pass")

surplus — a quantity or amount over and above what is needed or used; excess
    (from Latin *plus,* "more")

surrealism — a movement in 20th-century art and literature that depicts the inner world of fantasy and dreams by using distorted images
    (from Latin *res,* "thing")

surveillance — a close watch or guard
    (from French *veiller,* "to watch")

surveyor — a person who plots and measures boundaries
    (from Old French *veoir,* "to see")

sur-

A. Fill in each blank with a word from the word list.

1. The detectives had the suspect under 24-hour _____ .

2. Before he became the first president of the United States, George Washington was a _____ .

3. The swimmer _____ (ed) her record for the breast stroke.

4. Salvador Dali's painting of clocks melting all over a landscape is a famous example of _____ .

5. She decided that when she got married, she would keep her own _____ rather than taking her husband's.

6. The company added a 10-percent _____ for rush orders.

7. He wanted his own car and he was determined to _____ every obstacle in his way.

B. Circle the words that use *sur-* as a prefix meaning "above" or "over." Refer to a dictionary that shows word derivations.

sureness	surly	surreptitious
surface	surmise	surrogate
surfboard	surplice	surround
surfeit	surprise	surtax
surgeon	surrender	survive

C. Do the following on separate sheets of paper.

1. Look up examples of surrealist painting in an encyclopedia or art book. Copy part of one painting.

2. What do you have a surplus of? A surplus can be of feelings (like worries) or of things (like baseball cards). Write a paragraph describing your surplus and what you plan to do with it.

therm	**heat**

thermal
> of or relating to heat or temperature
>> (from Greek *therme,* "heat")

thermoelectric
> of or having to do with the direct relations between heat and electricity
>> (from Latin *electricus,* "produced from amber by rubbing")

thermometer
> an instrument used to measure temperature
>> (from Greek *metron,* "measure")

thermonuclear
> of a nuclear reaction that occurs only at high temperatures, such as nuclear fusion
>> (from Latin *nucleus,* "a nut, a kernel")

thermos
> a double-walled container with a vacuum between, used to keep substances at a constant temperature
>> (from Greek *therme,* "heat")

thermostat
> a device used to control temperature
>> (from Greek *states,* "one that causes to stand")

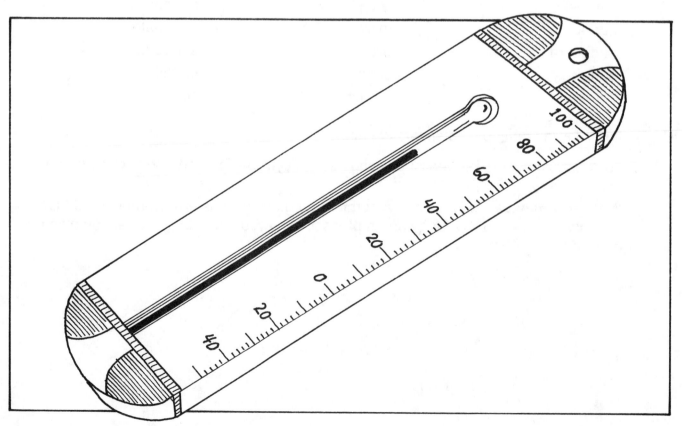

therm

A. Fill each blank with a word from the word list.

1. The _____ showed that she was running a temperature of 101°.

2. My mother put hot soup in my _____ for lunch.

3. A hydrogen bomb explosion is caused by a _____ reaction.

4. We keep our _____ at 62° to save energy and to lower the utility bill.

5. Most skiers wear _____ underwear.

B. Look up each of the following words in a dictionary and briefly define them.

1. thermograph _____

2. thermocouple _____

3. thermochemistry _____

4. therm _____

5. thermotropism _____

C. Do the following activities on separate sheets of paper.

1. How many thermostats do you have in your home? At what temperature is the thermostat set during the day in the winter? At what temperature is it set at night during the winter?

2. Draw a picture of yourself in thermal underwear under a thermal blanket in your bed.

Review Test 3

A. Circle the new root or prefix in each of the following words. Then write the meaning of the root or prefix in the blank after the word.

1. surmount _____

2. nondescript _____

3. portfolio _____

4. interrupt _____

5. malefactor _____

6. retrospective _____

7. thermostat _____

8. miscalculate _____

9. polysyllabic _____

10. omnipresent _____

11. primitive _____

B. Fill in each blank with prefix or root that will make a word to fit the definition.

1. _____ flammable   not easily set on fire

2. _____ active   going into effect as of a specified date in the past

3. _____ ometer   an instrument used to measure temperature

4. _____ ady   a disorder or disease

5. ex _____   to send goods to another country

6. dis _____   to break up or throw into confusion

7. _____ fit   someone who is badly adjusted to his or her environment

8. _____ vorous   eating both plants and animals as food

9. _____ pass   to be better or greater than

10. _____ gon   a closed plane figure with more than four sides or angles

11. _____ eval   of or relating to prehistoric times

Final Test

A. Circle the correct answer for each question.

1. Which figure has more sides?   **a pentagon**   **a decagon**

2. Which happens more often?   **a centennial**   **a triennial**

3. Which has more legs?   **a centipede**   **a millipede**

4. Which has more events?   **a decathlon**   **a pentathlon**

5. Which is longer?   **a centimeter**   **a decimeter**

6. Which is longer?   **a kilometer**   **a millimeter**

7. Which has more horns?   **a triceratops**   **a unicorn**

8. Which one is a boat?   **a hydroplane**   **a monorail**

9. Which one does good for others?   **a benefactor**   **a malefactor**

10. Which has more feet?   **a biped**   **a quadruped**

B. Circle the correct answer in each sentence below.

1. *Ject* in *eject* means   **to jump**   **to throw**   **to burst**.

2. *Ambi* in *ambivalent* means   **many**   **all**   **both**.

3. *Omni* in *omnipotent* means   **many**   **all**   **both**.

4. *Com* in *commiserate* means   **together**   **around**   **above**.

5. *Mis* in *misquote* means   **not**   **wrongly**   **out of**.

6. *Poly* in *polyhedron* means   **many**   **round**   **all**.

7. *Rupt* in *erupt* means   **to throw**   **to burst**   **to carry**.

8. *Ex* in *excavate* means   **out**   **away**   **former**.

9. *Sur* in *surcharge* means   **together**   **under**   **above**.

10. *Prim* in *primitive* means   **first**   **last**   **back**.

C. Complete each analogy with one of the words below.

Example: Four is to quadruple as one hundred is to *centuple* _____.

**circumference   hemisphere   malignant   nonflammable   omnivorous
polyglot   portfolio   primary   quadruped   retrorocket**

1. Car is to brake as spacecraft is to _____.

2. Happy is to sad as benign is to _____.

Wordstrength © 1989

3. Square is to perimeter as circle is to _____ .

4. Human is to biped as horse is to _____ .

5. Annual is to semiannual as globe is to _____ .

6. Side is to polyhedron as language is to _____ .

7. Water is to waterproof as fire is to _____ .

8. Knowledge is to omniscient as food is to _____ .

9. Businessman is to briefcase as artist is to _____ .

10. Second is to first as secondary is to _____ .

D. Fill in the blank in each sentence with one of the words listed below.

> **conjunction   credence   detrimental   dilemma   disparity
> interject   nonplus   quintessence   unilateral   thermal**

1. All through dinner, Tania pondered the _____ of whether to study some more for tomorrow's test or to work on her term paper.

2. With her blond hair and deep tan, she was the _____ of a California girl.

3. *And, but,* and *nor* are all _____ (s).

4. He didn't give _____ to the rumors.

5. Too little sleep can be _____ to your health.

6. Because of the _____ of their tastes, Veronica was never tempted to borrow her sister's clothes.

7. In subzero weather, it's a good idea to wear _____ underwear.

8. Since no one could agree, he made the _____ decision that they would go ice skating on Saturday.

9. The class decided to try to _____ the substitute teacher by refusing to speak to him.

10. Joel couldn't bear all his friends looking so gloomy, so he told a joke to _____ some humor into the situation.

Wordstrength © 1989

Answer Key

Pretest, page 6

A.   2. bi-
      7. cent-
    11. centi-
     6. deca-
    10. deci-
     9. demi-
     2. di-
     9. hemi-
     8. kilo-
     8. mill-
    12. milli-
     1. mono-
     5. penta-
     4. quadr-
     5. quint-
     4. tetra-
     3. tri-
     9. semi-
     1. uni-

B.   1. both
     2. good
     3. around
     4. together
     5. together
     6. to believe
     7. down
     8. not
     9. out
    10. water
    11. to throw
    12. bad
    13. wrongly
    14. not
    15. all
    16. many
    17. to carry
    18. first
    19. back
    20. to break
    21. above
    22. heat

mono-, uni-, page 8

A.   1. unicycle; 2. monogram; 3. unison;
     4. monotony; 5. unilateral

B.   1. monocle: a single lens held in front
      of the eye by the angle between the
      nose and the eyebrow
     2. uniform: not varying in form,
      quality, character, and so on
     3. universe: all the space, matter, and
      energy that is thought to exist
     4. monochrome: a painting or
      drawing in tones of one color
     5. unify: to make into one

C.   Answers will vary.

bi-, di-, page 10

A.   1. dipterous; 2. biceps; 3. dilemma; 4.
     bilingual; 5. bisect

B.   1. Biannual; 2. Biennial; 3. Bicenten-
     nial; 4. bimonthly; 5. biweekly

C.   Answers will vary.

tri-, quadr-, tetr-, page 12

A.   1. tricorn; 2. tetrachloride; 3. tripli-
     cate; 4. tetrahedron; 5. quadrangle

B.   D, 1; C, 2; A, 3; E, 4; F, 5; B, 6

C.   1.

      2.

      3.

penta-, quint-, page 14

A.   1. quintessence; 2. pentameter; 3.
     quintet; 4. pentathlon; 5. pentacle

B.   Answers will vary, but they may in-
     clude the following:
     hexa-: hexagon, hexagram, hexameter,

hexapod

ses-, sex-: sestet, sestina, sexennial, sextant, sextet, sextile, sextillion, sextuple, sextuplet

hepta-: heptad, heptagon, heptameter, heptarchy

sep-, sept-: September, septennial, septet, septilateral, septillion, septuple, septuplet

oct-: octad, octahedron, octameter, octane, octant, octave, octet, octillion, October, octopus, octuple

ennea-: ennead

non-, novem-: nonagon, nones, nonillion, November

C. 1.

2. Answers will vary.

deca-, deci-, page 16

A. 1. decimate; 2. decathlon; 3. decibel; 4. decimal; 5. decade

B. B,1; D, 2; C, 3; E, 4; A, 5; F, 6

C. 1. Answers will vary.
2. whisper, 10 decibels; jet plane, 100 decibels; rock music, 80 decibels; a 140-decibel sound is painful

demi-, hemi-, semi-, page 18

A. 1. demitasse; 2. semicolon; 3. Hemisphere; 4. semiannual; 5. demigod

B. The circled words are semiliquid, semiformal, semidetached, semimonthly, semiopaque.

C. 1. Answers will vary.
2. quaver=eighth note ♪

𝄾 semiquaver=sixteenth note

demisemiquaver=thirty-second note

hemidemisemiquaver=sixty-fourth note

cent-, centi-, page 20

A. 1. centigrade; 2. centennial; 3. centimeter; 4. centipede; 5. centuple

B. 5, centigram; 1, centiliter; 6, centimeter; 4, hectogram; 3, hectoliter; 2, hectometer

C. Answers will vary.

kilo-, mill-, milli-, page 22

A. 3, milligram; 5, kiloliter; 1, kilometer; 6, milliliter; 2, kilogram; 4, millimeter

B. 1. millisecond; 2. kilogram; 3. milliliter; 4. millimeter; 5. kiloton; 6. milligram

C. Answers will vary.

Review Test 1, pages 23–24

A. 1. centimeterworm; 2. decameter (or dekameter) line; 3. no prefix needed; 4. decaliter (or dekaliter); 5. hectoliterbasket; 6. kilogramcake; 7. fourdecaliter (dekaliter); 8. kilometer; 9. hectogram of prevention, kilogram of cure

B.

Name	# of groups of 3 zeros after 1,000
million	1
billion	2
trillion	3
quadrillion	4
quintillion	5
sextillion	6
septillion	7
octillion	8
nonillion	9
decillion	10

C. 1. dipterous; 2. biped; 3. centipede; 4. unicycle; 5. tetrahedron; 6. tricorn; 7. pentacle; 8. millipede; 9. octagon; 10. quadruped; 11. hexagon; 12. demisemiquaver

ambi-, amphi-, page 26

A. 1. ambidextrous; 2. Amphibian; 3. ambivalent; 4. ambiguous; 5. ambiance

B. 1. noun; the ability to use both hands equally well
    2. noun; opposite and conflicting feelings about something
    3. noun; the quality of having two or more possible meanings
    4. adjective; that can live or travel on both land and water
C. 1. The drawing should show the stages of egg, tadpole, and mature animal.
    2. Answers will vary.

ben, bene, page 28
A. 1. benefactor; 2. benediction; 3. beneficial; 4. beneficiary; 5. benign
B. The circled words are Benedict, benefaction, beneficence, benefit, benignant.
C. Answers will vary.

circ-, circum-, page 30
A. 1. circumvent; 2. circumnavigate; 3. circumspect; 4. circumscribe; 5.circulation
B. 1. of behavioral or physiological rhythms associated with the 24-hour cycle of the earth's rotation
    2. the scheme or system of an electric circuit
    3. a mark used over certain vowels in some languages to indicate a certain sound
    4. a roundabout or too lengthy way of speaking
    5. dealing with particular details or circumstances; secondary or not essential
C. 1. Answers will vary.
    2. circulating library: a library from which books can be borrowed
    circuit rider: a minister who travels from place to place in his circuit to preach
    circuit breaker: a device that automatically interrupts the flow of an electric current

circuit court: a state court having original jurisdiction in several counties or districts

com-, page 32
A. 1. combat; 2. companion; 3. compound; 4. compete; 5. compare
B. 5, compel; 7, complicate; 8, coma; 2, compartment; 4, comedy; 1, complex; 3, compromise; 6, comet. The circled words are compel, complicate, compartment, complex, compromise.
C. Answers will vary.

con-, page 34
A. 1. construction; 2. connect; 3. consent; 4. contend; 5. congregate; 6. convenient; 7. conjunction
B. 1. the arrangement of all the elements and details within a form
    2. an effect or result
    3. to plan secretly to do something unlawful; to combine or act together
    4. to change from a liquid to a jelly-like solid state, especially as the result of cooling
    5. able to be spread or passed on easily
    6. anything that is contained in something
    7. a general agreement
C. Answers will vary.

cred, page 36
A. 1. incredible; 2. credo; 3. credential; 4. credence; 5. credulous; 6. discredit
B. 1. with the promise that payment will be made later
    2. bringing approval or honor to one
    3. a person to whom money is owed
    4. disbelieving
    5. believability, reliability
C. Answers will vary.

de-, page 38

A. 1. deposit; 2. deflate; 3. desultory; 4. detrimental; 5. decline; 6. descend

B. 1. deactivate: to make inactive or reduce the activity of

debrief: to question soldiers, astronauts, or others who have returned from a mission, in order to assess their success

decode: to convert a code into the original message or form

desegregate: to end the separation of different races or sexes

2. defrost: to remove ice and frost from a refrigerator; to thaw frozen food

dehumidify: to remove moisture from the air

dethrone: to remove a monarch from the throne

dehydrate: to lose or remove water

C. Answers will vary.

dis-, page 40

A. 1. disequilibrium; 2. disparity; 3. dissimilar; 4. disadvantage; 5. disrespectful; 6. dissatisfied

B. 1. to take away weapons or means of attack; to overcome the suspicions or hostility of

2. to pay out

3. to allow to be seen or known

4. to reduce the price of something; to refuse to believe something

C. Answers will vary.

ex-, page 42

A. 1. exotic; 2. extinguish; 3. exude; 4. excavate; 5. exorbitant; 6. expel

B. 1. the partial or complete obscuring of one celestial body by another

2. to throw out forcefully; to compel to leave

3. to bring out; to call forth or bring to light

4. to leave one country or region to settle in another

5. to release or send forth; to utter

6. to wear away

C. 1. Answers will vary.

2. An emigrant (from *migrare,* "to move") is someone who has moved out of one place and into another, often by choice. An exile (from *al-,* "to wander") is someone who for some reason can no longer live in his or her country and who, consequently, does not have a home. An expatriate (from *patria,* "native land") is someone who has moved out of his or her native country and usually has also changed citizenship.

Although these three words have similar spellings, excise (from *caedere,* "to cut"), exercise (from *arcere,* "enclose, restrain"), and exorcise (from *horkos,* "oath") mean quite different things. Excise means to cut out. Exercise means to exert, to be active. Exorcise is to free from evil spirits.

hydr, hydro, page 44

A. 1. hydroplane; 2. dehydrate; 3. hydroelectric; 4. hydrant; 5. hydrophobia

B. 1. a microscopic freshwater animal

2. a colorless, odorless, flammable gas that forms water when combined with oxygen

3. the decomposition of a compound by water, with each new compound containing part of the water

4. the growing of plants without soil—in water or on wet sand or peat

5. having to do with hot water, especially the action of hot water in producing minerals and springs

C. 1. Answers will vary.

2. Answers may include acetylene, benzene, natural gas, gasoline, kerosene, paraffin, asphalt, coal tar, alcohol.

ject, page 46

A. 1. projectile; 2. abject; 3. eject; 4. trajectory; 5. conjecture; 6. interject

B. 1. project *(noun):* a scheme that is contemplated, devised, or planned for the future; a piece of work, involving research, given to a student or group of students
(verb): to protrude; to plan or intend; to throw; to unknowingly attribute one's own attitudes, etc., to others

2. adjective: any word that describes or adds to the meaning of a noun

3. injection: the forcing of a fluid into the body by means of a syringe or hypodermic needle

4. reject *(noun):* something that is rejected, refused, or discarded
(verb): to refuse to accept or to use; to throw away

5. interjection: a word or phrase used as an exclamation

6. object *(noun):* anything that can be seen, touched, or perceived by any of the senses
(verb): to disapprove of, dislike, or argue against

7. subject *(noun):* a topic or main theme; a person who owes allegiance to a sovereign or a government
(verb): to bring under some power or influence

C. Answers will vary.

Review Test 2, page 47

A. 1. excavate: out, out of
2. benefactor: good, well
3. disrespectful: not, without
4. incredible: to believe
5. deflate: down, down from
6. hydraulic: water

7. ambivalent: both
8. projectile: to throw
9. commiserate: together, with
10. circumference: around, circle
11. congregate: together, with

B. 1. de
2. hydr
3. dis
4. ambi
5. ex
6. com
7. circum
8. inter
9. bene
10. con
11. cred

mal-, page 49

A. 6, malnourished; 3, malefactor; 5, malignant; 1, malady; 2, malevolent; 4, malice

B. 1. poorly adjusted, especially of a person who cannot adapt to his or her surroundings or form relationships

2. a person who is discontented and inclined to rebel

3. a general feeling of unexplained discomfort or weakness

4. a recurrent disease transmitted by mosquitoes and causing fevers and chills (originally believed to be caused by the bad air of swamps)

5. a curse

6. to fail to work as it should

7. to pretend to be ill, especially in order to escape work

C. Answers will vary.

mis-, page 51

A. 1. misconstrue; 2. misnomer; 3. misfit; 4. miscalculate; 5. misquote; 6. mistrial

B. 1. unlucky accident
2. wrong or unlawful behavior
3. bad luck
4. to give wrong or misleading information
5. to lose something temporarily by forgetting where it was put
6. a mistake in printing
7. to give a false or misleading account or description of
C. Answers will vary.

non-, page 53
A. 1. nonflammable; 2. nonprofit; 3. nondescript; 4. nonconformist; 5. noncommittal
B. 1. any prose literature that is based on facts rather than created by the imagination
2. not standard, especially designating grammatical constructions or pronunciations that differ from standard speech
3. expressed without words, especially by gestures or facial expressions
4. abstaining from violence or the use of physical force
5. not restrictive, especially designating a clause, phrase, or word that is not essential to the sense and thus usually set off by commas
C. Answers will vary.

omni-, page 55
A. 1. omnivorous; 2. omniscient; 3. omnipresent; 4. omnifarious; 5. omnibus
B. 1. the possession of unlimited power
2. a creature that eats both plants and animals
3. unlimited knowledge
4. a pervasive presence
5. for sending and receiving radio or sound waves in or from any direction
C. Answers will vary.

poly-, page 57
A. 1. polyester; 2. polychrome; 3. polygon; 4. polygraph; 5. polyglot
B. 1. the state or practice of having two or more husbands at the same time
2. the state or practice of having several spouses or mates at the same time
3. the state or practice of having two or more wives at the same time
4. of music having two or more simultaneous voices or parts, each with its own melody, but all harmonizing
5. of a fat or oil lacking hydrogen bonds at several points in its carbon chain and thus reacting with other compounds
C. 1. pol-y-chrome; pol-y-glot; pol-y-gon; pol-y-graph
2. Answers will vary.

port, page 59
A. 1. comport; 2. portfolio; 3. deport; 4. rapport; 5. import; 6. purport
B. 1. transportation: a carrying of goods or passengers from one place to another
2. reporter: a person employed to collect and report or write about news
3. porter: a person employed to carry luggage, as in a railway station, airport, or hotel
4. supportive: giving loyalty, aid, or belief to
5. portable: that can be carried
C. Answers will vary.

prim, page 61
A. 1. primeval; 2. Primary; 3. primate; 4. prime; 5. primer; 6. primitive
B. 1. the line of longitude 0° through Greenwich, London, from which other measures of longitude are taken

2. a positive integer that is exactly divisible only by itself and 1, such as 5, 7, and 11
3. any color having no trace of another color
4. the official leading the government in certain countries, such as Australia, Canada, and England
5. the hours when the largest radio or TV audience is available, especially the evening hours
6. the principal woman singer in a concert or opera; a temperamental or theatrical person
7. a preliminary election held in each state to select candidates for the later election of the president

C. 1. 2, 3, 5, 7, 11, 13, 17, 19, 23, 29, 31, 37, 41, 43, 47, 51, 53, 59, 61, 67, 71, 73, 79, 83, 89, 97

2.

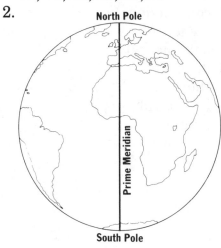

North Pole

Prime Meridian

South Pole

retro-, page 63

A. 1. retrogress; 2. retroactive; 3. retrospective; 4. retrograde; 5. retrorocket

B. 1. to ignite (a retrorocket)
2. a change in design, construction, or equipment, as of an aircraft or machine tool already in operation in order to incorporate later improvement
3. a backwards movement to a lower, less complex stage or state

4. a looking back, a survey of the past

C. Answers will vary.

rupt, page 65

A. 1. disrupt; 2. abrupt; 3. interrupt; 4. erupt; 5. corrupt; 6. bankruptcy; 7. rupture

B. 1. (adverb) suddenly or unexpectedly; discourteously or briefly
2. (noun) dishonesty, evil, or loss of innocence
3. (adjective) throwing into confusion; breaking up
4. (noun) a bursting or forcing out violently
5. (noun) a break in the continuity of

C. Answers will vary.

sur-, page 67

A. 1. surveillance; 2. surveyor; 3. surpass; 4. surrealism; 5. surname; 6. surcharge; 7. surmount

B. The circled words are surface, surfeit, surmise, surplice, surprise, surrender, surround, surtax, survive.

C. Answers will vary.

therm, page 69

A. 1. thermometer; 2. thermos; 3. thermonuclear; 4. thermostat; 5. thermal

B. 1. a thermometer for recording variations in temperature automatically; especially, an infrared camera for recording differences between normal and abnormal body tissues
2. a device consisting of two different conductors joined at each end, used for measuring temperature
3. the branch of chemistry studying the quantities of heat absorbed or produced by chemical reactions
4. a unit of energy

5. growth or movement toward or
   away from a source of heat
C.　Answers will vary.

Review Test 3, page 70
A.　1. surmount: above, over
　　2. nondescript: not
　　3. portfolio: to bring, to carry
　　4. interrupt: to break, burst
　　5. malefactor: bad, wrongful
　　6. retrospective: back, backward
　　7. thermostat: heat
　　8. miscalculate: badly, wrongly
　　9. polysyllabic: much, many
　　10. omnipresent: all
　　11. primitive: first

B.　1. non
　　2. retro
　　3. therm
　　4. mal
　　5. port
　　6. rupt
　　7. mis
　　8. omni
　　9. sur
　　10. poly
　　11. prim

Final Test, pages 71–72
A.　1. a decagon
　　2. a triennial
　　3. a millipede
　　4. a decathlon
　　5. a decimeter
　　6. a kilometer
　　7. a triceratops
　　8. a hydroplane
　　9. a benefactor
　　10. a quadruped
B.　1. to throw
　　2. both

3. all
4. together
5. wrongly
6. many
7. to burst
8. out
9. above
10. first
C.　1. retrorocket
　　2. malignant
　　3. circumference
　　4. quadruped
　　5. hemisphere
　　6. polyglot
　　7. nonflammable
　　8. omnivorous
　　9. portfolio
　　10. primary
D.　1. dilemma
　　2. quintessence
　　3. conjunction
　　4. credence
　　5. detrimental
　　6. disparity
　　7. thermal
　　8. unilateral
　　9. nonplus
　　10. interject